Sacred Conversations™

An Invitation to Dialogue with God

Dedication:

This journal is dedicated to the millions of Christians
who daily place themselves in harms way for the sake of the Gospel.
Every three minutes, one of our brothers or sisters in Christ
are martryed for their faith.

50% of the author's royalties for Sacred Conversations™
will go to support Voice of the Martyrs,
a ministry that serves the persecuted and their families.

© Lawson Falle Publishing Ltd.
Cambridge, ON, Canada
www.lawsonfalle.com
Made in Korea

Beloved Sister,

*I went into this project with fear and trembling, knowing well that the
Voice of God is far beyond anything our limited minds can comprehend. I do
believe however that, as we spend time in His Word and in His Presence,
He will confide in us and tell us things that we do not know (Psalm 25:14).
It is my prayer that this journal will only draw you closer to His throne, to
His voice and to His heart. Nothing matters more than our oneness with Jesus.*

*As you search for Him, may you find Him in a fresh new way. His mercies
are new every morning and His faithfulness is great.*

All for Him,

Susie M. Larson

General Journal Guidelines:

1.) *Don't* feel anxious about "fitting in" your writing time. This journal is meant to supplement your devotional time. It is here to serve you.
2.) *Do* tenaciously guard your time in God's Word. It is imperative that you be firmly rooted and planted so that you can stand strong in all seasons.
3.) *Don't* manipulate your faith to match your life. Allow your devotional times to draw you deeper into God's marvelous love. Be brave enough not only to write down your hopes and dreams, but to also chronicle the ways God is calling you higher.
4.) *Do* humble yourself every day before His mighty throne, and wait to hear His voice. He has many wonderful things to tell you.

Specific Guidelines for This Journal:

1.) This journal isn't meant to be used in perfect order; go to the page that best represents where you are at (i.e. fear, hope, expectation, etc.).
2.) Meditate on the Scripture provided at the top of the page.
3.) "Breathe" it in and allow the power of God's Word to stir in your soul.
4.) Read the prompted prayer below the verse; without thinking too much about it, continue the prayer in your own words. (Don't worry about grammar, punctuation or even 'how it sounds', let your words flow and pour your heart out to God!)
5.) The very next page contains a prompted response (to your previous prayer) from your Heavenly Father. Again, begin to write what you sense that the Lord has to say to you. *Be careful not to use this response time as a tool to try to get what you want from God. Rather, use this time to listen and respond to the ways He is calling you higher in your character.* Some of the common roadblocks to writing down God's responses are:
   a. Fear of getting it wrong
   b. Doubt
   c. Preoccupation with your problems
6.) Overcome these things by immersing yourself in the Word, by praying for the "mind of Christ" and by understanding that we only know in part right now – but God still longs to speak to us.
7.) As you draw near to God, He will draw near to you!

But I have stilled and quieted myself, just as a small child is quiet with its mother. Yes, like a small child is my soul within me.
Psalm 131:2 NLT

QUIETNESS...

Sovereign Lord,

I come before You today with a heart that longs to be close to Yours. I come to listen to what You have to say to me. I release, in Jesus' Name, all of my cares in Your presence. I will draw close to You and place my head on Your shoulder. As You wrap Your strong arm around me, I am reminded that I am safe, I am cared for and You are watching over me. Help me to release all of my roles and just be Your child for the moment. I will rest with You as You remind me...

that you love me and will take care of me. I want so badly to make a concious effort to learn and build a better relationship with you. I've been very lost lately and I'm coming to you with complete faith and love. Please help guide me in the right direction. Amen   12-28-09
          Love your child,
               Nicole

Precious Child,

Allow Me to speak peace into your soul. As you draw from the strength of My presence, your cup will become full once again. You don't always have to be in control, on duty and on the go. If you want protection from burnout, you must come to Me as a child...every day. I promise it will not be burdensome; it will be precious time well spent. Stay for a moment and let Me tell you...

I feel that I am carrying more than I can handle. I neglect myself and my faith to focus on everyone elses problems and I worry about their opinions too much. I need to focus on serving You and meeting my needs before anyone elses, I truly believe that my purpose is to help others. Please help me to continue discovering more of what You want from me. Open my eyes and my heart.   12-29-09

Love your child,
Nicole

Unto you O Lord, do I bring my life.
Psalm 25:1 AMP

DEPENDENCE...

Dearest Lord,

Today I come to You with all that concerns me. I know that You love me and are watching me closely. Help me now to express my thoughts, my thanks and my worries openly and honestly. I know that none of these things stress You out. It is good for me to cling tightly to You because You have everything under control. These are the things that are on my mind:

_____

_____

_____

_____

_____

_____

_____

_____

_____

_____

_____

_____

_____

_____

_____

Dependence

Precious Child,

I love to spend time with you. You are right you know - I will take care of all that concerns you. These burdens are not yours to carry; they are easy for Me, and so let Me have them. Instead, you carry faith, hope and trust. You will find much joy in the journey when you embrace the strength that comes with My love. I can be trusted. Listen to Me now. Today I want you to remember that...

_____

_____

_____

_____

_____

_____

_____

_____

_____

_____

_____

_____

_____

_____

_____

_____

_____

_____

_____

The Lord is my strength and my shield;
my heart trusts in him, and I am helped.
Psalm 28:7 NIV

STRENGTH TO STAND...

Dearest Lord,

Sometimes it feels like arrows are coming at me from all directions. Help me not to cover my head and hide. Help me instead to take up my armor and stand in the battle. If You are for me, who can be against me? I will determine to trust You even when all of my senses tell me to be afraid. I know that I need to let go of a few things; show me Lord, exactly what they are:

_____

_____

_____

_____

_____

_____

_____

_____

_____

_____

_____

_____

_____

Strength to stand

Precious Child,

Though the storm rages, remember that I rule the storm. Remember that you are not home yet; the journey seems long but will be worth it in the end. I promised you that hard times would come, but I also promised to go with you through the storm. There is nothing I will allow to come your way except that which will cultivate My likeness in you. Lean on Me, trust in Me and know that every trial has its limits and this too shall pass. In the meantime, look at the areas in your life that are being purified right now. I am...

_____

_____

_____

_____

_____

_____

_____

_____

_____

_____

_____

_____

_____

_____

_____

_____

_____

_____

But whatever I am now, it is all because God has
poured out his special favor on me...
1 Corinthians 15:10a NLT

HUMILITY...

Precious Father,

When I ponder the fact that You left a beautiful throne room to enter a darkened womb; You left peace and took on poverty; You left a place where You were revered and exalted, to go to a place where You'd be cast down and trampled on...all for the sake of love, it takes my breath away. How could I ever come up with an ounce of pride when I'm reminded who You are and what You've done? In Your Name, Jesus, I cast down any selfish pride and I fully embrace the truth that anything good in me comes from You. Forgive me for thinking that I...

_____

_____

_____

_____

_____

_____

_____

_____

_____

_____

_____

_____

_____

_____

Humility

Precious Child,

It is for your safety and your care that you know how fragile you are without Me. But with Me, you'll find great strength; you'll see lives changed, mountains moved and land recovered. I love you, precious child, and it's imperative that you see yourself the way I do. The minute you trust in yourself and your strengths, you are at risk of falling - and child, you can fall from any level. Guard your humble heart with everything you have in you. Be careful not to trust in...

_____

_____

_____

_____

_____

_____

_____

_____

_____

_____

_____

_____

_____

_____

_____

_____

_____

_____

_____

Don't be impatient for the Lord to act!
Travel steadily along his path.
Psalm 37:34a NLT

IMPULSIVE...

Faithful Father,

Help me to have the endurance and the vision to continue on the path You've set before me. Help me not to grab for quick solutions and counterfeit answers. Give me the grace to live out my faith with honor and consistency. Your Word tells me not to give under impulse; help me too, not to live under impulse. You are not an impulsive God; You are fully in control, possessing great wisdom. Help me, Lord, to...

_____

_____

_____

_____

_____

_____

_____

_____

_____

_____

_____

_____

_____

_____

Impulsive

Beloved Child,

You are right to desire a consistent walk of faith. More troubles are wrought by hasty decisions than this world can imagine. Impulsive, hasty decisions come from a lack of faith and a loss of spiritual vision. I am never bound by your calendar or your timeline. I won't be. I am, on the other hand, fully able to move heaven and earth on your behalf. And I will do this for the faithful, trusting heart. I want you to trust me in...

_____

_____

_____

_____

_____

_____

_____

_____

_____

_____

_____

_____

_____

_____

_____

_____

_____

_____

Do not abandon me, Lord. Do not stand at a distance, my God.
Come quickly to help me, O Lord my Savior.
Psalm 38:21-22 NLT

DESPERATE...

Gracious Father,

*I need You right now. My soul clings to You as I wait for You to help me.
Give me a sense of Your nearness, Lord. Help me to remember in the darkness
what You told me in the light. I need a glimpse of Your purpose for me so that
my heart will not faint. I know that You are totally in control even if it doesn t
feel that way today. Right now, Lord, I am anxious about...*

_____

_____

_____

_____

_____

_____

_____

_____

_____

_____

_____

_____

_____

_____

_____

_____

Desperate

Precious Child,

I still hold you in My hands. Though it feels like you are forsaken, you must believe otherwise. There is a limit to what I'll allow My children to walk through. The world is full of sin and wretched pain. I have been there; I know. I have felt the things you feel and My heart aches for you. But I am not worried about you because I know that you'll come forth as gold as you trust in Me. Refuse worry and doubt; instead, exercise your faith. Believe Me now for...

_____

_____

_____

_____

_____

_____

_____

_____

_____

_____

_____

_____

_____

_____

_____

_____

_____

_____

Therefore, since we are receiving a kingdom that cannot be shaken,
let us be thankful, and so worship God acceptably
with reverence and awe, for our "God is a consuming fire."
Hebrews 12:28 NIV

PRAISE...

Holy Father,

Forgive me for the times that I have taken You for granted. Forgive me for praying half-hearted prayers while forgetting that when I stand before You, I am on holy ground. May I never get so busy that I forget who it is that I serve and love and get my life from. You are God, and You deserve my highest praise. I will praise You when life is hard; I will praise You when life is good; I will praise You in all things because...

_____

_____

_____

_____

_____

_____

_____

_____

_____

_____

_____

_____

_____

To My Child, Whom I Love,

When you acknowledge My strength and power in your life...your faith will grow. When you praise Me in the valley, your eyes will be lifted to a heavenly perspective. Never cease to praise Me; it is not always easy, but it is always right. When you worship and praise Me with a pure heart, I am right there in the midst of it all! I will take a demanding, entitled spirit and transform it to one of humility and thankfulness. As you praise Me, you will hear Me, and I will show you...

_____

_____

_____

_____

_____

_____

_____

_____

_____

_____

_____

_____

_____

_____

_____

_____

_____

_____

_____

And God has actually given us his Spirit (not the world's spirit)
so we can know the wonderful things God has freely given us.
1 Corinthians 2:12 NLT

REMIND ME AGAIN...

Father God,

*My mind cannot begin to grasp all of the things You have freely given to me.
So often I forget what I already possess and I waste energy grabbing for the
counterfeit. Holy Lord, remind me again, who I am in You. Remind me
always of this truth: the very power that raised Christ from the dead, is alive
in me! Help me to sit here and soak in all of potent truths that I have
forgotten about...*

_____

_____

_____

_____

_____

_____

_____

_____

_____

_____

_____

_____

_____

Remind me again

Precious Child,

How I love and adore you. You are right; there is much in the heavenlies that you've yet to take hold of. When My truths become your core beliefs, everything will change in your life. Your limited mind cannot grasp what I have made available to you, but a believing heart will open the floodgates of heaven! Believe Me when I say, I love you; I have a plan for you and I long to do powerful things through you. Listen to Me now as I speak to your heart; I want to increase your faith for...

_____

_____

_____

_____

_____

_____

_____

_____

_____

_____

_____

_____

_____

_____

_____

_____

_____

_____

Give thanks to the Lord, for he is good;
his love endures forever.
Psalm 118:29 NIV

THANKFULNESS...

Gracious Father,

You are good. You are so very good. Give me a thankful heart this day. When I embrace a heart of gratitude, I chase away the clouds of worry, doubt and fear. You inhabit the praises of Your people. As I lift up praises and thanks to You, perspective comes and I feel joy once again. When I begin to count my blessings, I find that they are too numerous to count! Thank you Lord for saving me, thank you for...

_____

_____

_____

_____

_____

_____

_____

_____

_____

_____

_____

_____

_____

_____

Thankfulness

Precious Child,

I love to give to My children! So often My gifts are missed, overlooked or passed over. Nevertheless, I give because I love you. How it pleases Me though when you 'stay close to home' and remember who your Source is. If you can hold onto gratitude, a demanding spirit will be far from you. It is good for your heart; it is good for your health and it makes Me smile when you say thanks. Today, I want you to notice...

_____

_____

_____

_____

_____

_____

_____

_____

_____

_____

_____

_____

_____

_____

_____

_____

_____

_____

_____

When doubts filled my mind,
your comfort gave me renewed hope and cheer.
Psalm 94:19 NLT

DOUBTS...

Dear Lord,

When doubts have overtaken my thought life and I am sure that all is lost, I must remember who You are. You are the God of all comfort and You are my God! How easy it is to forget Your provision when I take my eyes off of You; and yet, how quickly I am restored when I remember who my Father is. Come Lord Jesus and fill my thoughts again...

Doubts

Sweet Child,

I love to bring comfort to your soul and hope to your heart. Your mind cannot even comprehend the help that is available to those who keep their eyes on Me. As you draw near to Me, I will draw near to you. As you understand Who I Am, you will begin to tremble in My Presence...this is when I will confide in you and tell you things that you do not know. Filling your mind with doubts is a waste of your precious time; fill your mind instead with My Power and...

_____

_____

_____

_____

_____

_____

_____

_____

_____

_____

_____

_____

_____

_____

_____

_____

_____

_____

_____

...May those who love you rise like the sun at full strength!
Judges 5:31b NLT

RENEWAL...

Precious Father,

This is a new day - fill me up to over flowing gracious God. Help me to see this day through Your eyes. Thank you for providing new mercies every morning. Your faithfulness is great and I am blessed by You. Each new day has its own special blessings. When my heart is thankful, my heart is happy. Today I want to thank You for...

_____

_____

_____

_____

_____

_____

_____

_____

_____

_____

_____

_____

_____

My Child,

I created the mornings so you would have a daily reminder of My fresh mercies. I make all things new and I am doing that for you today. As you count your blessings, your joy increases. I will pour Myself afresh on you as you come to Me for renewal. Sit with Me and gain a fresh perspective on your life; notice how I have...

_____

_____

_____

_____

_____

_____

_____

_____

_____

_____

_____

_____

_____

_____

_____

_____

_____

He calmed the storm to a whisper and stilled the waves.
Psalm 127:29 NLT

CHAOS...

Dear Lord,

When things feel out of control and I feel that I've lost my bearings, help me to look to You. You will take on my storm and give me peace. As I look at the wind and the waves in my life, it seems they threaten to swallow me up; but when I fix my gaze upon You, the storms don't matter as much. You rule the storms and You will change my chaos into order. Show me how things got this way; speak to my heart...

_____

_____

_____

_____

_____

_____

_____

_____

_____

_____

_____

_____

_____

Chaos _____

Precious Child,

I will stretch out My hand for you. As you release control and reach for Me, I will take control; that is when the peace arrives. Call on My Name and I will answer you. Do not be afraid and do not let your scattered feelings rule you. Instead, speak out the things you know to be true - like the facts that you are loved, valuable and cared for. Write them down and recite them from your heart. I love you, I...

_____

_____

_____

_____

_____

_____

_____

_____

_____

_____

_____

_____

_____

_____

_____

_____

_____

_____

_____

Bear with each other and forgive whatever grievances you may have
against one another. Forgive as the Lord forgave you.
Colossians 3:13 NIV

FORGIVING OTHERS...

Dear God,

*My heart aches when I remember the things others have done to hurt me.
Sometime it's hard not to think too much about it all. And yet I know I too,
have broken Your heart when I have hurt others. I need Your Supernatural
Power to change my heart and help me stand. May Your forgiveness flow in
me and through me always. As I search my heart, I am reminded of the
offenses that I need to lie at Your feet...*

_____

_____

_____

_____

_____

_____

_____

_____

_____

_____

_____

_____

_____

_____

_____

Forgiving Others

Precious Child,

I know how you feel and I care deeply about you. I can help you with forgiveness. As you give Me your hurts and offenses, I will give you health and healing. As you bring Me the lies that are in you, I will replace them with the Truths that will set you free. In due time, you will learn how to pray for your offenders. You will have compassion on them and see them through My eyes. You will be able to do this because you will understand to your core that they don't get to decide how precious you are...I do. Now take this moment to remember...

Take control of what I say, O Lord,
and keep my lips sealed.
Psalm 141:3 NLT

GOSSIP...

Oh Father God,

I come to You with a great burden in my soul. I need You Lord, to purify my heart and mind. Help me to speak only those things which are consistent with heaven's voice. You are gracious, kind and faithful; help me to be that way. Pour out Your Spirit upon me so that the words that flow from me bring only encouragement and healing. Forgive me for...

_____

_____

_____

_____

_____

_____

_____

_____

_____

_____

_____

_____

_____

_____

Gossip

Beloved Child,

Your words are prayers and if you want to stay in a place of peace and unity, your prayers must be in agreement with Me. All too often, words are justified, denied and swept aside, but their impact leaves deep wounds and scars in the hearts of My children. It breaks my heart to watch My own injure one another this way! And yet, My heart swells with pride when you find the courage to stop the flow, stand for scorned and refuse the bandwagon. I want you to come to a higher level with Me. I want your words to consistently reflect My heart...

May integrity and uprightness protect me,
because my hope is in you.
Psalm 25: 21 NIV

UPRIGHTNESS...

Dear Lord,

I know that You are continuously calling me higher. I pray with each new day, my life would reveal that I have spent time with You. As long as I walk this earth, I know there will be areas in my life that You want to redeem. Help me not to run away every time You have something difficult to say to me. I know that You only want to make me more like You. I have a sense that You've been speaking to me about ...

_____

_____

_____

_____

_____

_____

_____

_____

_____

_____

_____

_____

_____

Uprightness

Precious Child,

I take such delight in a heart like yours. I have heard your prayers and am working all things together for your good. I am busy and active in ways that you cannot see. I only want you to be full and free, and you will be as you continue to respond to My work in your life. Every time you trust and obey, you will come to know, in a deeper way, that I am your stronghold. As I work in your life, I ask that you would take hold of these promises...

_____

_____

_____

_____

_____

_____

_____

_____

_____

_____

_____

_____

_____

_____

_____

_____

_____

_____

Listen to my voice in the morning, Lord.
Each morning I bring my requests to you and wait expectantly.
Psalm 5:3 NLT

AN EXPECTANT HEART...

Precious Lord,

*Today, I come and I lift my hands before You. Fill me to overflowing.
Take my fears, my mistakes and my ramblings and give me Your peace. As I
sit in Your presence, I breathe in all of Your life-giving power and I exhale all
of the thoughts that are not of You. I will not run today to other sources
when You are all I need. I wait for You to fill me and to speak to me today...*

_____

_____

_____

_____

_____

_____

_____

_____

_____

_____

_____

_____

_____

_____

_____

An Expectant Heart

Precious Child,

I absolutely adore you. I want you to know that I love to love you! Each day, I have something new to tell you. Sometimes I'll speak through a song or through the breeze, or better yet, through a child. Your eyes and ears must be attentive to My voice. I am always speaking...are you always listening? Draw yourself closer to Me and find rest instead of rushing, peace instead of pressure. Today, I want to tell you...

_____

_____

_____

_____

_____

_____

_____

_____

_____

_____

_____

_____

_____

_____

_____

_____

_____

_____

May the Lord bring you into an ever deeper understanding
of the love of God and the endurance that comes from Christ.
2 Thessalonians 3:5 NLT

DEEPER LOVE...

Dear Savior,

You left a most holy place and handed Yourself over to evil for me. My mind cannot comprehend the love that compelled You to do such a thing. How I want to have a deeper understanding of Your ways and Your heart towards people. Your love is reckless and abundant, mine is measured and contingent. Pour out Your Spirit upon me and increase my capacity to give Your love away. Show me what, in my life, hinders Your light from fully shining through me...

_____

_____

_____

_____

_____

_____

_____

_____

_____

_____

_____

_____

_____

_____

_____

_____

Deeper Love

To My Child, Whom I Love,

I delight to answer a prayer like yours. I will pour My love on you in ways that will surprise you. Often, these provisions come in unusual packages. Never limit your expectation of when and where I will show up. I will always draw the seeking heart to a deeper place; this is rarely comfortable, but always an adventure. Listen to Me now as I speak to you; I would like you to...

_____

_____

_____

_____

_____

_____

_____

_____

_____

_____

_____

_____

_____

_____

_____

_____

_____

_____

Fear of man will prove to be a snare,
but whoever trusts in the LORD is kept safe.
Proverbs 29:25 NIV

OTHER'S OPINIONS...

Dearest Lord,

Help me not to put a lot of energy into others' estimation of me. What matters most is that I follow You and listen to Your voice. You are the One that I have to face when life on earth is through, and You are the One I'm ultimately accountable to. May I be so in touch with Your calling on my life that I make choices which clearly cooperate with Your plan for me. Protect me from my tendency to think and act and choose because (or so that) someone might think...

_____

_____

_____

_____

_____

_____

_____

_____

_____

_____

_____

_____

_____

Other's Opinions

Sweet, Sweet Child,

Keep this request at the forefront of your prayers always. If you let your guard down, you'll begin to do things for the wrong reasons. As much as I love My children, their opinions about you matter very little. Your own opinions change with the wind, so put no stock in others' assessments of you! Others do not get to decide your value...unless you say they can. I love you, I value you and I will take you to the next place I have for you. Today, I want to tell you what I think of you...

_____

_____

_____

_____

_____

_____

_____

_____

_____

_____

_____

_____

_____

_____

_____

_____

_____

_____

The foundations of heaven tremble at his rebuke. His Spirit made
the heavens beautiful, and his power pierced the gliding serpent.
These are some of the minor things he does, merely a whisper of his power.
Who can understand the thunder of his power?
Job 26:11, 13-14 NLT

JUSTICE...

Dearest Lord,

*Sometimes it seems as though the evil prosper and the godly suffer. You are in
control and yet the irreverent, wicked heart flies in the face of Your holiness.
How long, O Lord, will You wait to humble the wicked and rescue Your
suffering children? No matter what my eyes may see, though, I will choose to
trust You. We have only seen a glimpse of Your power; there will come a time
when You'll be revealed in all of Your fullness. Then, everyone will know
that You are all powerful, the Captain of the Hosts, and You are definitely in
control. In the meantime, I believe You are calling me to...*

_____

_____

_____

_____

_____

_____

_____

_____

_____

_____

_____

_____

_____

Justice

Precious Child,

I know that I may appear as a sleeping giant to the irreverent, wicked heart. The truth is, though, that I am busy and active in the lives of my humble, hungry children. My return tarries because of my heartfelt love for the people I have created. Always remember, the wicked aren't "getting away" with anything. Every scale will be balanced in the end. Soon, I'll return and there will be no missing it. Every knee will buckle at the breath of My command; some in horror and some with great excitement, because I really Am who I say that I Am. Time is running out; be aggressive in your pursuit of and obedience to Me. I want you to...

_____

_____

_____

_____

_____

_____

_____

_____

_____

_____

_____

_____

_____

_____

_____

_____

_____

A gentle answer turns away wrath, but a harsh word
stirs up anger.
Proverbs 15:1 NIV

ANGER...

Precious Lord,

I need You now; in fact I need You every hour. When I am stepped on, walked over or shoved aside, first I ache, and then I get mad. Oh Lord, please sanctify my heart, my mind and my words. I will trade You this anger for some of Your precious peace. In order to embrace Your likeness in my life, help me to willingly lay down...

_____

_____

_____

_____

_____

_____

_____

_____

_____

_____

_____

_____

_____

_____

Anger _____

Wounded Child,

I fully understand and I know right where you are. I couldn't love you more if I tried. I will lead you as we walk through the fire, but you will have to trust Me. At times, I allow the fire because it brings impurities to the surface. During these times you will have to choose whether you will point at another's imperfections, or humbly bring Me your own. Overwhelming victory and supernatural power are available to My children when they humble themselves and pray...

_____

_____

_____

_____

_____

_____

_____

_____

_____

_____

_____

_____

_____

_____

_____

_____

_____

Listen, for I have worthy things to say; I open my lips to speak what is right.
Choose my instruction instead of silver, knowledge rather than choice gold...
Proverbs 8:6, 10 AMP

CHOICES...

Dear God,

My days get to be so full. Before I know it, I have spent my energy on things that You said You would take care of. All You have asked of me is that I keep my eyes on You, learn from You and do the things that YOU tell me to. I must confess, I often get pulled in other directions because...

_____

_____

_____

_____

_____

_____

_____

_____

_____

_____

_____

_____

_____

_____

Choices

My Child,

I love you so much and I will show you the way to go. It breaks My heart when My children run to and fro with such anxiety over their busy schedules. I never called My children to be busy, just obedient. Sometimes that involves a measured busy-ness, but always it includes an inner rest and peace. I want you to listen for My voice, because I can see the whole map and I know the best way for you. Keep listening for My voice; today I want you to remember...

_____

_____

_____

_____

_____

_____

_____

_____

_____

_____

_____

_____

_____

_____

_____

_____

_____

_____

Don't just do what you have to do to get by, but work heartily,
as Christ's servants doing what God wants you to do.
And work with a smile on your face, always keeping in mind that
no matter who happens to be giving orders, you're really serving God.
Ephesians 6:6-7 MSG

WORKING FOR HIM...

Awesome Father,

*At times it's hard to believe that I can make much of a difference in my world.
But when I think of the boy who gave You his lunch, I am reminded that You
multiplied his little offering and fed a multitude of people. Give me a heavenly
perspective in my work today. Help me to bring dignity and honor into the
things I do and say. Confirm to me, why what I do is important to You...*

_____

_____

_____

_____

_____

_____

_____

_____

_____

_____

_____

_____

_____

Working For Him

Faithful Child,

Think about this. If the generous boy would have given his lunch to somebody else, that would have been charitable, and someone would have been fed at his expense. But since he gave what he had to Me, his gifts were multiplied beyond belief, everyone ate until they were full, and there was much left over! That's the difference between working alone and working with Me. You want to see families, neighborhoods and cities changed? Use your gifts for Me and watch what I will do through you. I want to use your gifts to...

_____

_____

_____

_____

_____

_____

_____

_____

_____

_____

_____

_____

_____

_____

_____

_____

_____

_____

The works of his hands are faithful and just;
all his precepts are trustworthy.
Psalm 111:7 NIV

TRUST...

Lord,

You know my heart's desires. You know what I am hoping for and dreaming about. And yet, I say by faith: Thank you, Lord, that You'll not bring these things to me a day sooner than I am ready for them. I don't want one blessing that my character can't handle. I don't want one breakthrough that will lead me away from Your throne. I trust You to...

_____

_____

_____

_____

_____

_____

_____

_____

_____

_____

_____

_____

_____

_____

_____

Trust _____

My Wonderful Child,

I am walking with you daily and I love to bless you. I am protecting you more than you know. As you humble yourself before Me, I will lift you up and make you a blessing. As you acknowledge your need before Me, I will meet needs in and through you. You are in the right place, humbly trusting Me. Breakthroughs are coming at just the right time. Watch and see...

Don't pick on people, jump on their failures, criticize their faults – unless, of course, you want the same treatment. That critical spirit has a way of boomeranging. It's easy to see a smudge on your neighbor's face and be oblivious to the ugly sneer on your own.
Matthew 7:1-3 MSG

A CRITICAL SPIRIT...

Have Mercy Oh Lord!

How wretched it must be to watch Your children spew criticisms when You died to cover them! When I even look away from the Vine, it seems that my flesh rules the day. I fall down on my face before You and I ask for Your forgiveness. I confess my sin of looking at certain people with a heart that is far from Yours. All of Your children are sacred to You and I have no business forming a hardened opinion toward any of them. Forgive me for...

_____

_____

_____

_____

_____

_____

_____

_____

_____

_____

_____

_____

Beloved Child,

This is a critical point in the walk of a believer. When you take up an offense, you've simply decided to stop growing. All of the religious busy-ness in the world will not advance your standing in the spirit when you carry an offense against another. On top of that, you cut off the Spirit's flow in your life and you pave an inroad for the enemy to get to you. It's never worth it and it's always wrong. I am aware of the foibles and inconsistencies in others; these are My problems, not yours. However, as you have come to Me in humility and repentance, I offer you deep forgiveness and mercy. I am calling you now to a higher way...

_____

_____

_____

_____

_____

_____

_____

_____

_____

_____

_____

_____

_____

_____

_____

_____

For I am the Lord your God, who stirs up the sea, causing its waves to roar.
My name is the Lord Almighty.
Isaiah 51:15 NLT

SMALL FAITH...

Oh God,

*How often I lose sight of your Holy power. Help me to see the bigger picture.
The very fact that you can stir up the sea and cause giant waves to roar
reminds me that You are not of this world. You are greater, higher and deeper
than my little mind can conceive. I need to pray with YOU in mind. I need a
gift of faith right now, faith to believe that You are...*

_____

_____

_____

_____

_____

_____

_____

_____

_____

_____

_____

_____

_____

_____

Small Faith

Precious Child,

My eye is on you and you are never beyond My grasp. I will open the eyes of your heart so you will know in your soul that I am the One who stills the storm and brings you safely in. Never lean on your own understanding nor cling to things with white knuckles. Open your hands in faith and give Me free reign in your life. I can be trusted. Over time, you will see this, and your faith will grow...

_____

_____

_____

_____

_____

_____

_____

_____

_____

_____

_____

_____

_____

_____

_____

_____

_____

_____

If you do what is right, will you not be accepted?
But if you do not do what is right, sin is crouching at your door;
it desires to have you, but you must master it.
Genesis 4:7 NIV

SIN...

Holy Father,

Keep me close to Your heartbeat and protect me from wandering away. Help me to remember that I am flirting with danger when I allow myself to go to the edge of what I know is wrong. Give me the wisdom to build a margin around my life so that I have room to respond when temptation comes my way. Show me, even now, what weaknesses in me make me susceptible to falling. Give me the courage to honestly come to You for help...

_____

_____

_____

_____

_____

_____

_____

_____

_____

_____

_____

_____

_____

Sin

Beloved Child,

I have given you everything you need to live a life of godliness and holiness. Overwhelming power and victory are yours because of Calvary. I will always provide a way out when temptation comes your way. Your part is to walk with Me daily, to stay grounded in My Word, to submit to Me even when you don't feel like it, and to pray for a heart that loves righteousness more than sin. I want you to ask Me for more...

_____

_____

_____

_____

_____

_____

_____

_____

_____

_____

_____

_____

_____

_____

_____

_____

_____

_____

_____

Yes, hear us from heaven where you live, and when you hear, forgive.
2 Chronicles 6:21b NLT

FORGIVE US!!!

Dearest Lord,

I pray today, on behalf of Your children everywhere. We are selfish to the core and we need Your mercy. Forgive us for pursuing personal comforts at the expense of sacrificial living. Forgive us for allowing hunger, when we ourselves are full. Forgive us for forgetting to pray for our suffering brothers and sisters while we make our plans and dream our dreams. Oh Lord, hear us from heaven, and forgive us...

_____

_____

_____

_____

_____

_____

_____

_____

_____

_____

_____

_____

_____

_____

_____

_____

Forgive Us

My Child,

There is much power in a prayer like yours. How I long for all of My children to lift their eyes and gain a global perspective. I have called you all to remember that you are part of a bigger family. When one suffers, the rest suffer. Parts of the Body are cared for, while others walk in poverty. This is never how I meant for it to be. My power is released through earnest prayers, and I will surely answer yours. This is what I long to see in my Church...

_____

_____

_____

_____

_____

_____

_____

_____

_____

_____

_____

_____

_____

_____

_____

_____

_____

Because The Sovereign Lord helps me, I will not be dismayed.
Therefore, I have set my face like a stone, determined to do his will.
And I know that I will triumph.
Isaiah 50:7 NLT

DETERMINATION...

Sovereign Lord,

You have made me what I am. You know all about me. You are aware of my weaknesses and my strengths. All that I have comes from You. Take my hand now and help me through this hour and this day as I face the task before me. As the enemy presses in to tell me that I'll never make it, may I resolve all the more not only to make it, but to triumphantly represent You in all that I do. Help me to keep my eyes on You and my heart believing Your truths. These things I know to be true...

_____

_____

_____

_____

_____

_____

_____

_____

_____

_____

_____

_____

_____

_____

Determination

Precious Child,

Take this time to come into My Presence with the realization that I Am all that you will ever need. I'm not just enough; My resources are exceedingly, abundantly beyond anything you can comprehend or even begin to exhaust. Nothing on earth compares to what I have available to my children. All of heaven is cheering for you as you press on to do My will. Don't think for a moment, that I won't give you more than you need to walk triumphantly through this life. I Am, I Have and I Will take care of you. The wisdom that I have for you today is this...

_____

_____

_____

_____

_____

_____

_____

_____

_____

_____

_____

_____

_____

_____

_____

_____

_____

Turn my heart toward your statutes and not toward selfish gain.
Turn my eyes away from worthless things;
renew my life according to your word.
Psalm 119:36-37 NIV

MATERIALISM...

Powerful Lord,

You are holy, pure and righteous. There is nothing that compares with You.
Protect me from the seduction of things that satisfy for a moment, but in the
end leave me empty. Father, You are all that I need. Your resources are endless
and Your promises are true. Help me to be repelled by the thought of grabbing
for myself. My life is preserved when it is found in You. I must confess, these
are the things that I've been clinging tightly to...

_____

_____

_____

_____

_____

_____

_____

_____

_____

_____

_____

_____

_____

_____

Materialism

Beloved Child,

Always remember that you are royalty. You have access to riches in the heavenly places and you are positioned to change the world around you. I have gone to the depths for you and willingly so. Tap into the resources that I have for you. Develop a taste for the fruits of the Spirit, and the world's candy will be as junk food to you. As you freely give, I will freely give you...

_____

_____

_____

_____

_____

_____

_____

_____

_____

_____

_____

_____

_____

_____

_____

_____

_____

_____

The generous prosper and are satisfied;
those who refresh others will themselves be refreshed.
Proverbs 11:25 NLT

GENEROSITY...

Loving Father,

You have been a perfect example in every way. You have shown me what it means to give sacrificially. Help me always to remember that when I hold what is mine with an open hand, I am walking in freedom. Help me too, to remember that when I cling to my precious possessions, I lose sight of their purpose in my life. Show me the ways that I can be more generous; show me what things I am clinging to besides You...

_____

_____

_____

_____

_____

_____

_____

_____

_____

_____

_____

_____

_____

_____

_____

Generosity

Royal Child,

So many of My children hinder ministry by hoarding that which was meant for others. My resources are endless and are there for the asking. Ask Me to help you feed the hungry and I will. Ask Me to help you free those in bondage and I will. Ask me to fulfill every selfish desire, and I won't. I care more about your character, our oneness and the needs of the broken, than anything else. Still, you will receive more from Me than you could ever gather on your own. I will give endlessly to you and through you when you ask in My Name and for the cause of Christ. Ask Me for...

_____

_____

_____

_____

_____

_____

_____

_____

_____

_____

_____

_____

_____

_____

_____

_____

_____

Surely resentment destroys the fool, and jealousy kills the simple.
Job 5:2 NLT

JEALOUSY...

Faithful Father,

Protect me from the jealous heart. I don't want to possess one, and I don't want to encounter one. I know that whenever I am counting my deficits instead of my blessings, I am a prime candidate for a jealous heart. I also know that when (in my own insecurity) I draw attention away from You and to myself, I may stir up a jealous heart. I am responsible for my actions and I am responsible to guard my heart. I bow before you this day with a humble, thankful heart. Help me to want what I already have; help me to...

_____

_____

_____

_____

_____

_____

_____

_____

_____

_____

_____

_____

_____

Jealousy

Precious Child,

Oh, how I love you! I will surely answer this prayer. It is very near and dear to My heart. Always remember that peace and discontentment cannot exist together. Choose thankfulness and discontentment will flee; then peace will come. Sit before Me now and recount all of the ways I have been faithful to you. Everyone has times of plenty and times of struggle. I am Lord of them all. You were made for better things; not to want someone else's blessings, but to be a blessing. I am transforming you right now as I show you...

_____

_____

_____

_____

_____

_____

_____

_____

_____

_____

_____

_____

_____

_____

_____

_____

_____

_____

I urge, then, first of all, that requests, prayers, intercession and thanksgiving be made for everyone-- for kings and all those in authority, that we may live peaceful and quiet lives in all godliness and holiness.
This is good, and pleases God our Savior,
I Timothy 2:1-3 NIV

AUTHORITY...

Sovereign Lord,

We live in a day when respect for authority is almost extinct; and yet I know that authority is a serious issue to You. Remind me, Lord, to pray hard for those in authority over me. It is too easy to find fault with leaders without even offering to be part of a solution. This is wrong and You have called me to a higher way. You are in control, and You have called me to pray for and appreciate those who carry the leadership load. Today, I pray for...

_____

_____

_____

_____

_____

_____

_____

_____

_____

_____

_____

_____

_____

Authority

Beloved Child,

This is an issue that is very close to my heart. An army can't operate without a clear understanding of their chain of command. My warring angels are powerful and effective because they know who they are accountable to. In this irreverent age, much evil goes on in our own camp because My children misunderstand what authority means to Me. This rouses My anger because it is a drain on My leaders. Pray for your government, pray for your church and pray for your family; if they can comprehend this point, they will be effective indeed. I want you to...

_____

_____

_____

_____

_____

_____

_____

_____

_____

_____

_____

_____

_____

_____

_____

_____

_____

_____

_____

But the Lord is faithful; he will make you strong
and guard you from the evil one.
2 Thessalonians 3:3 NLT

STRENGTHEN ME...

Faithful Father,

Sometimes the battle seems too difficult for me. At times I feel that I am in over my head. I need to remember that You are truly faithful. I know that as I yield my life to You, You will build Your strength in me. As I hide myself in You, I will find You to be my stronghold, my strength and protection. Help me to put away any thoughts that weaken me; I lay down, in the Name of Jesus, thoughts such as...

_____

_____

_____

_____

_____

_____

_____

_____

_____

_____

_____

_____

_____

_____

_____

Strengthen Me

My Warrior Child,

I am the most powerful force on earth and yet I deal gently with My children. I can stir up the ocean with no effort and yet I'll handle your fears with great care. Those who humbly turn to Me have My fullest attention; you are precious to Me and you are different today than you were yesterday. You are stronger than you think. I will continue to build My character in you. Meditate on My promises, for they will make you strong. I promise to...

_____

_____

_____

_____

_____

_____

_____

_____

_____

_____

_____

_____

_____

_____

_____

_____

_____

_____

When doubts filled my mind,
your comfort gave me renewed hope and cheer.
Psalm 94:19 NLT

DOUBTS...

Dear Lord,

*When doubts have overtaken my thought life and I am sure that all is lost,
I must remember Who You are. You are the God of all comfort and You are
my God! How easy it is to forget your provision when I take my eyes off of
You; and yet, how quickly I am restored when I remember who my Father is.
Come, Lord Jesus, and fill my thoughts again...*

_____

_____

_____

_____

_____

_____

_____

_____

_____

_____

_____

_____

_____

Doubts _____

Sweet Child,

I love to bring comfort to your soul and hope to your heart. Your mind cannot even comprehend the help that is available to those who keep their eyes on Me. As you draw near to Me, I will draw near to you. As you understand Who I Am, you will begin to tremble in My Presence...this is when I will confide in you and tell you things that you do not know. Filling your mind with doubts is a waste of your precious time; fill your mind instead with My Power and...

_____

_____

_____

_____

_____

_____

_____

_____

_____

_____

_____

_____

_____

_____

_____

_____

_____

He will cover you with his feathers, and under his wings you will find refuge;
his faithfulness will be your shield and rampart.
You will not fear the terror of night, nor the arrow that flies by day,
Psalm 91:4-5 NIV

FEAR...

Faithful Father,

*As wickedness in the world increases, and as bad things continue to happen
to good people, I find it hard at times not to fear. But Your Word instructs me
over and over again to trust in You. You have seen it all, and nothing
overwhelms You. Life seems to hang on by a thread, things can happen in a
moment's time; I guess this is why we must live by faith. You have given me
everything I need to live a life of freedom. I confess as sin the choice of
embracing fear when You've given me enough reason for faith. Forgive me
for fearing...*

_____

_____

_____

_____

_____

_____

_____

_____

_____

_____

_____

_____

_____

Fear

Beloved Child,

You have just taken hold of a mystery that eludes so many of My children. All too often, people run from fear, make choices out of fear and allow fear to rule their lives. But when you stop and face it head on, when you confess fear as sin and a lack of trust...faith comes. One of Satan's greatest tactics against you is to stir up fear; and this battle will not be over until I bring you home with Me. So until then, you must learn how to fight for your freedom in Me. Take hold of...

_____

_____

_____

_____

_____

_____

_____

_____

_____

_____

_____

_____

_____

_____

_____

_____

_____

_____

But in that coming day, no weapon turned against you will succeed.
And everyone who tells lies in court will be brought to justice.
These benefits are enjoyed by the servants of the Lord;
their vindication will come from me, I, the Lord have spoken!
Isaiah 54:17 NLT

FACING EVIL...

Powerful Lord,

*I will find my hiding place in You. I cannot face this foe alone, but I can do
ALL things when You strengthen me. You are my stronghold, You are my
deliverer and You will cover me as I walk through this dark valley. Take me
to that higher place where I can see Your face and rest in Your great care. My
greatest weapon against evil is Your pure and humble love. These things I
declare in Your Name...*

_____

_____

_____

_____

_____

_____

_____

_____

_____

_____

_____

_____

_____

_____

Facing Evil

My Warrior Child,

While it's true that you're fighting a battle, you are not fighting it alone. If you could see in the Spirit, you would see thousands of warring angels, mounting their horses on your behalf. Do not step out on your own strength. Keep your heart humble and pure. Let no evil offense take up residence in your soul. Guard your heart with all of the tenacity you have in you. If you do these things, you will come through this battle with more insight, more faith and a greater awareness that I Am who I say I Am. Here is your battle strategy; pray for more...

The righteous face many troubles,
but the Lord rescues them from each and every one.
Psalm 34:19 NLT

RESCUE ME!

Powerful Lord,

I need to be reminded today of Your great ability to save. Take me to that higher place, dear Lord. Help me to see a way out or a way through. I know that everything You bring me through has merit and purpose. How can I obey You here? Give me ears to hear Your wisdom for me today. Show me...

_____

_____

_____

_____

_____

_____

_____

_____

_____

_____

_____

_____

_____

_____

_____

Rescue Me

Wonderful Child,

I will show you the way that you should go. That you would turn to Me with all of your concerns blesses My heart beyond measure. Never have I forsaken those who seek after Me. I will not let you out of My sight. Soon, this trial will be over and you will be the richer for it. Take a moment today and count your blessings in this valley. Remember that I will...

_____

_____

_____

_____

_____

_____

_____

_____

_____

_____

_____

_____

_____

_____

_____

_____

_____

_____

_____

Praise the Lord, I tell myself, and never forget the good things he does for me. He forgives all my sins and heals all my diseases. He ransoms me from death and surrounds me with love and tender mercies.
He fills my life with good things. My youth is renewed like the eagle's!
Psalm 103:2-5 NLT

HEALING...

Oh Lord,

How I long to be redeemed and restored. Sometimes it takes forever to see change or improvement; at least it seems that way. I need You right now; please give me a greater sense of Your presence. Right here, in the midst of my waiting, I declare You to be faithful, true and loving. You have my best interest at heart and You will surely come for me. My life will not always be like this; this season shall pass and brighter days are ahead. Heal my mind, my heart, my soul and my body. Heal me through and through. I wait, Oh Lord, for You to...

_____

_____

_____

_____

_____

_____

_____

_____

_____

_____

_____

_____

Healing _____

Priceless Child,

I love you and am watching you more closely than you can imagine. I've assigned you angels for protection; they love and care about you too! The very power that raised Me from the grave, is ALIVE in you! Spend this "waiting room" time exercising your faith, asking for more faith and remembering the ways I have been faithful in the past. I am a faithful God and I will not forsake you. As you press in to Me during this trial, I will give you a greater understanding of My ways and plan for your life. You are not a victim; you are a victor! I am Your Redeemer and Healer and I want you to remember...

_____

_____

_____

_____

_____

_____

_____

_____

_____

_____

_____

_____

_____

_____

_____

_____

Know that the Lord is God. It is he, who made us,
and we are his; we are his people, the sheep of his pasture.
Psalm 100:3 NIV

ACCEPTANCE...

Dear God,

It can be so easy to get caught up in the thinking of this world. The world measures our stature by outward appearances and by what we produce. You look upon the heart. Help me, Lord, to embrace my value in You whether things are happening for me or not. You are never ashamed to claim me as one of Your own. That is an amazing gift. I am thankful to belong to You; this gives me great comfort. Help me to understand this wonderful truth today. If I am honest with myself, I would have to say that these are the things that I often look to - to define me...

_____

_____

_____

_____

_____

_____

_____

_____

_____

_____

_____

_____

_____

_____

Acceptance

Precious Child,

I love to call you My own. Understanding this truth (or not) will determine where you end up in your life's journey. More than anything, I want you to stretch your arms open wide and receive My love with the reckless abandon of a child. I am God; I made you and I will not forsake you. I love you. Never let these truths out of your mind; think about them day and night. Today I want to tell you...

_____

_____

_____

_____

_____

_____

_____

_____

_____

_____

_____

_____

_____

_____

_____

_____

_____

_____

_____

Keep me from lying to myself;
give me the privilege of knowing your law.
Psalm 119:29 NLT

DENIAL...

Faithful Lord,

It is very painful sometimes, to look deep inside myself at the issues that weaken me and keep me from growing. But with You at my side, and the assurance of Your great love, I come to You today. Shine Your light in my heart and show me if I have a blind spot or an area where I have been unwilling to grow. Give me a profound understanding of Your powerful Word that I may be transformed from glory to glory! As I sit before You, show me...

_____

_____

_____

_____

_____

_____

_____

_____

_____

_____

_____

_____

_____

Denial

Beloved Child,

Your prayer is a courageous one. Rest assured, when I speak to your heart, it will resonate with you. You will know that I am right about the things I am showing you. When the enemy of your soul speaks, he comes at you with belittling labels, names and predictions. My words will bring hope, inspiration and encouragement. His will bring despair, doubt and discouragement. Never confuse the two. The more you walk with Me, the more you'll be in tuned with My voice. Today, I want you to look at...

_____

_____

_____

_____

_____

_____

_____

_____

_____

_____

_____

_____

_____

_____

_____

_____

_____

_____

He floods the darkness with light;
he brings light to the deepest gloom.
Job 12:22 NLT

DEPRESSED...

God in Heaven,

I need You right now. Please move the dark clouds from me and let me see the blue sky once again. I know You are there and I know You care for me. Cup Your hands around me, Lord, and protect me from the elements. I am weary and empty and I need Your help. You are Lord and You are in control. Bring light to my darkness and fill me with joy afresh. I confess my anxieties to You now...

_____

_____

_____

_____

_____

_____

_____

_____

_____

_____

_____

_____

_____

_____

_____

Depressed

Beloved Child,

I am right here, and I won't leave you. You are in My arms and I will carry you. I promise You this: this valley will not last forever and I WILL bring you through it. Rest in My care and let Me lead you day by day, moment by moment. I will deal gently with you and I will increase your faith. I will do these things for you. There is something, though, that only you can do. You must take your thoughts captive and make them consistent with heaven's voice in your life. Sanctify your thought life, it's your only hope for survival; replace your negative thoughts with...

_____

_____

_____

_____

_____

_____

_____

_____

_____

_____

_____

_____

_____

_____

_____

_____

_____

God sets the lonely in families, he leads forth the prisoners with singing; but the rebellious live in a sun-scorched land.
Psalm 68:6 NIV

LONELY...

Caring Father,

What was it like for You to walk this earth, knowing full well that even Your best friends would run when You needed them most? It must have been deeply lonely not to have one person who truly understood You. I imagine Your heart ached for Your reunion with your Father in heaven. Yes, You know how I feel. Help me to remember this in my soul. Just because I feel lonely, doesn't mean I am alone. I have a loving Savior watching over me and ten thousand angels singing my song. When it seems that no one is pursuing me, I have to remember that You always are. I am not alone. I will not be imprisoned by how I'm feeling at the moment. I will stand on the fact that...

_____

_____

_____

_____

_____

_____

_____

_____

_____

_____

_____

_____

_____

Lonely

Beloved Child,

Oh how I love you! I want you to embrace the lonely days as a different kind of friend. They are there to remind you that I Am your Source; not your friends, nor your busy schedule, not even all the great things you do for Me. I am your Source and you can daily draw new life from Me. If you want a cure for your loneliness, go visit the shut-in, the terminally ill or the orphan. One day blends into the next for them and they need encouragement for the journey. Sing to them, read to them and encourage them. When you do it for them, you do it for Me. Today, I challenge you to...

_____

_____

_____

_____

_____

_____

_____

_____

_____

_____

_____

_____

_____

_____

_____

_____

_____

Whoever walks with the wise will become wise;
whoever walks with fools will suffer harm.
Proverbs 13:20 NLT

FRIENDSHIPS...

Faithful Father,

There is no friend like You. You never betray, backstab or belittle. Your thoughts and Your posture towards me are always those of love and faithfulness. You are endlessly wise. Help me, Lord, to be that kind of friend. Help me too, to choose friendships that bear fruit. Every day on this earth is a gift from You, and I want my ways and my days to count. Speak to me, Lord, about my friendships...

_____

_____

_____

_____

_____

_____

_____

_____

_____

_____

_____

_____

_____

Friendships

My Child, My Friend,

As you walk closely with Me, I will confide more and more in you. As you give your whole heart to Me, I will make you a powerful friend, one that ministers wisdom, encouragement and healing. At least half of the people you walk with should be wiser and godlier than you. The rest should be challenged and inspired by your pursuit of Me. Run from relationships that foster negativity, critical spirits and prideful judgments. I want you to...

_____

_____

_____

_____

_____

_____

_____

_____

_____

_____

_____

_____

_____

_____

_____

_____

_____

_____

Who among you fears the Lord and obeys his servant?
If you are walking in darkness, without a ray of light,
trust in the Lord and rely on your God.
Isaiah 50:10 NLT

NEEDING A BREAKTHROUGH...

Faithful Father,

I need You right now. I can't see in front of me, it's too late to turn back and I am wondering if I'm even on the right path. How I want to be full of faith right now, Lord, but instead I am weary. I need a gift of encouragement this day - something that will confirm that I am moving in the right direction. But even if You choose not to show Yourself at this point...I will still trust You. You are still God; You are still on Your throne and You are still very much in control. I will trust You. I lay these things down at Your feet...

_____

_____

_____

_____

_____

_____

_____

_____

_____

_____

_____

_____

My Dear Child,

You are right when you say that I am still in control. I am not anxious about your situation and you don't need to be either. When you cease to depend on what your earthly eyes can (or cannot) see, then your Spiritual eyesight will get sharper and more focused. As your faith grows and your Spiritual eyesight becomes keener, you will become equipped to thrive in the next place I have for you. I am strengthening you, I am...

_____

_____

_____

_____

_____

_____

_____

_____

_____

_____

_____

_____

_____

_____

_____

_____

_____

_____

Since you have been raised to new life with Christ, set your sights on
the realities of heaven, where Christ sits at God's right hand
in the place of honor and power. Let heaven fill your thoughts.
Do not think only about things down here on earth.
Colossians 3:1-2 NLT

LOOK ABOVE IT...

Faithful Father,

*When I become overwhelmed with the tasks of the day and I allow my
anxious thoughts to overtake me, I find myself forgetting who You are to me.
When my eyes become fixed on the waves and the wind, I forget that You rule
the storm. Oh how I always want to remember that the storms don't dictate
my life - You do. You are seated in the place of honor and power and when I
look to You, I find that I...*

_____

_____

_____

_____

_____

_____

_____

_____

_____

_____

_____

_____

_____

Look Above It

Precious Child,

Whenever you find yourself overwhelmed by the obstacle - look above it. Whenever fear looms about you - look above it. Whenever chaos threatens to overtake you - look above it, and say My Name. Fix your eyes on Me and say My Name. I am always here for you. When it feels that I am far away, especially then, keep your eyes on things above. I will surely come and save you. There is no higher authority than Me, and all other forces recognize that. So when My children call out My Name, I will...

_____

_____

_____

_____

_____

_____

_____

_____

_____

_____

_____

_____

_____

_____

_____

_____

_____

_____

_____

Cling tightly to your faith in Christ, and always keep your conscience clear.
1 Timothy 1:19 NLT

CLEAR CONSCIENCE...

Holy Lord,

The longer I live, the more I realize how desperately sinful I am. I need You every single hour of every single day. Have Your way in my life - make me more and more like You. As I cling tightly to the Vine, purify my heart from selfish motives, jealous actions and prideful thoughts. Only You can turn my heart around so that out of it flows a river of life. Your Word says that those who have neglected a clear conscience have shipwrecked their faith. I don't ever want to do that. With great humility, I bring you my thoughts...

_____

_____

_____

_____

_____

_____

_____

_____

_____

_____

_____

_____

_____

_____

_____

Clear Conscience

Precious One,

I will keep you close to Me and I love to do so. As you dare to draw near to Me with all of your imperfections, I will draw near to you and lead you to a higher place. My Spirit recognizes even the slightest departure from holiness and when you walk next to Me, you'll notice it too. It's when My children go their own way, and do their own thing that they become calloused to the stirring of their conscience. I have given you a gift in that inner voice; hold it in high regard as you walk closely with Me. I want you to take time to...

_____

_____

_____

_____

_____

_____

_____

_____

_____

_____

_____

_____

_____

_____

_____

_____

_____

_____

The righteous will move onward and forward,
and those with pure hearts will become stronger and stronger.
Job 17:9 NLT

MOVING FORWARD...

Blessed Lord,

I don't want to live a life that appears busy but bears little fruit. All that I do will bear more fruit if I regularly come to You - humbly and reverently - and in my coming, I respond to Your dealings with me. When I have the courage to allow Your hand of discipline to point out my unrighteousness and my less-than-pure motives, (and I have the willingness to respond to You), then I will move forward and grow stronger. Help me today to cease from pointing at others and to allow You, instead, to point to me. What in me, Lord...

_____

_____

_____

_____

_____

_____

_____

_____

_____

_____

_____

_____

_____

_____

Moving Forward

Cherished Child,

You will live a powerful life and take more ground than most when you guard against busy-ness and respond to My voice in your life. Nothing comes to you by accident. Use every blessing and every attack to choose the Christ - like way. As you pursue purity and righteousness and as you walk in love, it will eventually become natural to respond the way I would. Today I want you to be honest before Me, and I will be honest with you. Let's talk about your weak areas (not to bring you shame, but to bring protection because that is where you are vulnerable). These are the areas I want to redeem...

_____

_____

_____

_____

_____

_____

_____

_____

_____

_____

_____

_____

_____

_____

_____

_____

_____

Those who plant in tears will harvest with shouts of joy.
They weep as they go to plant their seed,
But they sing as they return with the harvest.
Psalm 126: 5-6 NLT

SOWING IN TEARS...

Faithful Father,

When life is hard and everything seems to have gone cold, it is easy to let go of what's important. If I have to let go of things that are dear to me, help me at least not to let go of the seed that says: though I can't see You now, I will come through this having found You abundantly. Though I feel empty and alone, I will soon be walking in fullness again. In times of pain I am tempted to grab hold of the wrong things for security. Help me only to grab hold of You, Lord. Help me to...

_____

_____

_____

_____

_____

_____

_____

_____

_____

_____

_____

_____

_____

_____

_____

_____

Sowing In Tears

Beloved Child,

I want you to know in the depths of your soul...that it is a big deal when My children trust Me with their pain. I cherish and greatly reward those who seek after Me. Always remember, I know all about pain and loss; you are not alone ...not even for a minute. Hang in there and press on, for it is in the fiery trials where your faith is perfected and your motives are purified. If you hang onto your seed of faith, you will come forth carrying a harvest that will carry you in the days ahead. Remember that I...

_____

_____

_____

_____

_____

_____

_____

_____

_____

_____

_____

_____

_____

_____

_____

_____

_____

_____

Stay alert; be in prayer so you don't wander into temptation without even
knowing you're in danger. There is a part of you that is eager,
ready for anything in God. But there's another part that's
as lazy as an old dog sleeping by the fire.
Matthew 26:41 MSG

WEAKNESSES...

Dear Lord,

*Protect me in my weak and vulnerable moments. I am capable of messing up
in so many ways when I wander from my fellowship with You. Motivate me
to stay alert, to be in prayer and to guard my time with You. As uncomfortable
as it may be, take my weaknesses and make them my strengths. Show me the
areas in my life where I am vulnerable and help me to courageously submit
those areas to You...*

_____

_____

_____

_____

_____

_____

_____

_____

_____

_____

_____

_____

_____

Weaknesses

Wonderful Child,

You would do well to remember that you are never more powerful against your foes, than when you are humbly on your knees before Me. You alone are no match for the enemy of your soul; he is not out to irritate you; he's out to destroy you. He trembles and shakes though when he sees My children calling out My Name. It is in My chamber where you'll find strength for your weakness, peace for your anxiety and defense against your enemy. I am your hiding place; hide yourself in Me. Right now, I want you to...

_____

_____

_____

_____

_____

_____

_____

_____

_____

_____

_____

_____

_____

_____

_____

_____

_____

_____

Live well, live wisely, live humbly.
It's the way you live, not the way you talk, that counts.
James 3:13 MSG

LIVING RIGHT...

Dear Lord,

There are a million good things that I could do with my time...then there are the BEST things. I want my life to fulfill all the things You had in mind when You created me. Help me to spend less time talking about the right things and more time doing them. Give me a heart that cares for the same things that You do. Today I sense that the BEST things for me to do would be...

_____

_____

_____

_____

_____

_____

_____

_____

_____

_____

_____

_____

_____

_____

Living Right

Precious Child,

I will not only help you; I will guide you and bless you for living a life that is good. It pleases My heart when you press in and seek the higher way. I am aware of all the things that you could do with your time. Stay close to My heartbeat and I will show you the things you should do. These are the things that will make the most difference for My Kingdom - these are the things that I want you to put your energy towards. Today I want you to...

_____

_____

_____

_____

_____

_____

_____

_____

_____

_____

_____

_____

_____

_____

_____

_____

_____

_____

_____

But the Lord is in his holy Temple; the Lord rules still from heaven.
He watches everything closely, examining everyone on earth.
Psalm 11:4 NLT

FIND ME FAITHFUL...

Faithful Lord,

When I imagine myself standing with the multitudes before You, as we each lay our crowns at Your feet; I realize that the only things I can offer You are those that I've done solely for You. How many things I have done for me! I don't think I could bear it to have to look into Your beautiful eyes and tell You I spent most of my energy on myself. Save me from myself, fill me up to overflowing, give me clean hands and a pure heart so that I can serve You fully...

_____

_____

_____

_____

_____

_____

_____

_____

_____

_____

_____

_____

_____

_____

_____

Find Me Faithful

Precious Child,

I WILL fill you up to overflowing and I delight to give you a heart like Mine. As the earth's clock continues to tick, the world's view of what's important will become more and more skewed. Right has become wrong and wrong has become right. To serve Me with a pure heart is to dare to live and stand for the things I have called you to. You will have to swim upstream to hold fast to My principles but you will have My supernatural power on your side. I want you to be radical for Me, and right now that starts with...

_____

_____

_____

_____

_____

_____

_____

_____

_____

_____

_____

_____

_____

_____

_____

_____

_____

_____

Guide me in your truth and teach me, for you are God my Savior,
and my hope is in you all day long.
Psalm 25:5 NIV

HOPE...

Faithful Lord,

Whose ways are higher than Yours? There is not one. People will disappoint me, plans will fail, things will get broken, but You, dear Lord, are unshakeable. You are higher than the heavens and deeper than the sea. Your plans are far - reaching and You are watching over me. I know it's okay to get excited about Your plans for me; but may my hope always be in You. Help me not to look to...

_____

_____

_____

_____

_____

_____

_____

_____

_____

_____

_____

_____

_____

_____

_____

Hope _____

Treasured Child,

When you keep your mind on things above, you'll keep your hope alive. There is much to be excited about! I plan to do great things in and through you. Never lose that childlike anticipation of what I will do next. I love it when you are inspired and thrilled about Kingdom work. Disappointment comes when you decide on your own how things should come about. Lift your eyes up to Me and keep your hands open. Let Me define your journey; you won't be disappointed. I want you trust Me in...

_____

_____

_____

_____

_____

_____

_____

_____

_____

_____

_____

_____

_____

_____

_____

_____

_____

_____

Dear brothers and sisters, whenever trouble comes your way,
let it be an opportunity for joy. For when your faith is tested,
your endurance has a chance to grow. So let it grow,
for when your endurance is fully developed,
you will be strong in character and ready for anything.
James 1:2-4 NLT

ENDURANCE...

Father God,

Help me to look at life through Your eyes; then I'll remember that I am a work in progress. As much as I try to avoid the uphill climb, it is there that my spiritual muscle and endurance are formed. You are with me through it all and I have nothing to fear. Everything that comes my way is measured through Your hands and will work towards my perfection if I will only yield myself to You. I can't give up; I must keep my eyes on the prize. I need to remember...

_____

_____

_____

_____

_____

_____

_____

_____

_____

_____

_____

_____

_____

Endurance

Precious Child,

To grow in strength and character, one must push beyond what's natural and comfortable. It is for your best and for My glory that I am calling you to the uphill climb. If you're not reaching for something that is beyond you, what is faith for? Believe it or not, you've only scratched the surface of what you are capable of. I have great plans for you; be excited about this! Choose the inner joy that is not contingent upon circumstance. Choose to believe that I...

_____

_____

_____

_____

_____

_____

_____

_____

_____

_____

_____

_____

_____

_____

_____

_____

_____

_____

The LORD is my light and my salvation--whom shall I fear?
The LORD is the stronghold of my life--of whom shall I be afraid?
Psalm 27:1 NIV

PROTECTION...

Lord,

You are everything to me. Jesus, You're the perfect King. You are my light; You'll show me the way. You are my salvation; my eternity is safe with You. You are the stronghold of my life; no matter what threatens me, You will have the final say. You will only allow that which will make me more like You. I can fully trust You and my heart is blessed. Even when I am afraid, I know that...

_____

_____

_____

_____

_____

_____

_____

_____

_____

_____

_____

_____

_____

_____

Protection

Precious Child of Mine,

You are right when you say that everything you need is found in Me. Spend as little energy as possible engaging in fear and worry, for they will steal your vitality and sap your strength. I did promise that life would be hard so try (as best as you can) not to be disillusioned by that fact. You were not made for this place; you were made for a far better land. This journey is only preparing you for your final destination. Use every opportunity to refuse anxiety by hiding yourself in Me. As I lead you, I want you to learn...

_____

_____

_____

_____

_____

_____

_____

_____

_____

_____

_____

_____

_____

_____

_____

_____

_____

Teach me your way, O LORD, and I will walk in your truth;
give me an undivided heart, that I may fear your name.
Psalm 86:11 NIV

AN UNDIVIDED HEART...

Dearest Lord,

I can spend much time doing all sorts of good things, and somehow still be out of Your divine will for me. As I give my time to things that You didn't ask me to do, I find myself feeling scattered, tired and unfulfilled. There are a million things I should care about, and yet I am only one person; I must hear from You and carry out the plan that You've assigned me to. Oh Lord, I don't want to waste this precious gift of time! I want to be sure of and focused on Your plans for me. I don't want to miss the mark. As I sit in Your presence, well up within me Your vision for me, and show me, too, what in my life needs to go...

_____

_____

_____

_____

_____

_____

_____

_____

_____

_____

_____

An Undivided Heart

Appointed Child,

All too often, My children rush to and fro from one thing to the next, never asking if it was theirs to do in the first place. What a powerful army of believers I will have when everyone carries out their appointed tasks! This is very important: The vision for your life is not fulfilled overnight; it takes time. I may tell you that you will live in the west, but in the meantime I may send you east. It's not for you to question your preparation, but do keep asking for clarity of your vision. As your focus becomes clearer, your resolve to choose wisely will become stronger. This is what I am calling you to...

_____

_____

_____

_____

_____

_____

_____

_____

_____

_____

_____

_____

_____

_____

_____

_____

_____

Don't grieve God. Don't break his heart. His Holy Spirit,
moving and breathing in you, is the most intimate part of your life,
making you fit for himself. Don't take such a gift for granted.
Ephesians 4:30 MSG

PLEASING GOD...

Heavenly Father,

*How desperately I want to please You. Help me not to be an earthbound
creature who gets lost in the daily grind. You have given me so much -
help me to take nothing for granted. Help me to greet each new day with a
wonder and amazement that You love me and You have something for me
to do. May Your Holy Spirit inspire me to cooperate with You today...*

_____

_____

_____

_____

_____

_____

_____

_____

_____

_____

_____

_____

_____

Pleasing God

Precious Child,

How I love you! Every day is a beautiful gift, and it's for your sake that I want you to notice what I am doing all around you. Every sunrise has My Name on it; every time the wind blows, I had something to do with it; every bite of food you eat, I have provided. I provide for you and through you. Don't miss all of the ways I am at work in your life. When you keep your eyes wide open, your faith will be strengthened and you will be encouraged. Today I want you to notice...

_____

_____

_____

_____

_____

_____

_____

_____

_____

_____

_____

_____

_____

_____

_____

_____

_____

_____

The horses are prepared for the battle,
but the victory belongs to the Lord.
Proverbs 21:31 NLT

PREPAREDNESS...

Fairest Lord Jesus,

You have called me to the work of exercising my faith, understanding and using my spiritual armor and of faithfully carrying out the burden You have placed on my heart. I am to be a soldier, not a spectator. If I live to feed my desires, I will become soft and ineffective. On the other hand, when I say "no" to my selfish desires, stand against evil and fight the good fight, I will become strong and prepared. Over all of this, though, I must remember that You will bring the victory and You will work in and through me. You are calling me higher and preparing me to be a lean soldier by...

_____

_____

_____

_____

_____

_____

_____

_____

_____

_____

_____

_____

Preparedness

My Warrior Child,

It is true; things that comfort the flesh often weaken the spirit. I want you to stand strong when the battle comes. I have told you that I will be with you, but I have also told you to take your stand and guard your heart. Are you doing that? Are you stronger today than you were a year ago? Exercise your faith daily. What are you believing me for right now? Remember your armor daily; is your shield of faith easy to handle? Is your sword sharp? Does your helmet fit your head? Do you have an eternal mindset? We have much to do together! Stay on the path I have for you. I want to teach you to...

_____

_____

_____

_____

_____

_____

_____

_____

_____

_____

_____

_____

_____

_____

_____

_____

_____

Be on guard. Stand true to what you believe. Be courageous. Be strong.
And everything you do must be done with love.
1 Corinthians 16:13-14 NLT

AGAINST THE FLOW...

Precious Father,

As we come closer to the end of time, it is more important than ever that I live life not as a reaction to what comes my way, but with intention, purpose and strength. Your Word says that, in the latter days, the love of most will grow cold; more than anything, I don't want to be one of the "most." This means I need the strength to go against the current of evil that pervades my world. Help me Lord, to stand strong and true, and to do all things with a heart of love. Give me courage to...

_____

_____

_____

_____

_____

_____

_____

_____

_____

_____

_____

_____

_____

_____

Against the Flow

Precious Child,

You are my joy. I love you so much. I will keep you strong and I will give you courage. Do not get distracted and pulled into battles that are not yours to fight. Nothing will drain you faster than doing things you're not appointed to do. I am the One who decides that for you; so spend time with Me and sit long enough to hear My response. I will never lead you astray. I know the best way for you and I will give you everything you need to get there. As we look together at where you are spending your time, I want to say this to you...

_____

_____

_____

_____

_____

_____

_____

_____

_____

_____

_____

_____

_____

_____

_____

_____

_____

_____

"If you don't go all the way with me, through thick and thin,
you don't deserve me. If your first concern is to look after yourself,
you'll never find yourself. But if you forget about yourself
and look to me, you'll find both yourself and me."
Matthew 10:38-39 MSG

GO ALL THE WAY...

Father God,

*I don't want to drag my feet, look back or look down. I have decided to
follow You and I want to finish strong. I have made You my Savior, and I
once again declare You as my Lord. You get to decide the direction of my life.
I am at Your service. I lay down selfish ambition, envy and pride. I pick up
the Sword of the Spirit and a humble heart. I am reminded that in this world,
You guaranteed I would have many troubles, but You promised to be with me
through them all. I am heaven bound; give me strength for the journey. Help
me to...*

_____

_____

_____

_____

_____

_____

_____

_____

_____

_____

_____

Go All the Way

Precious Child,

I am leading you and will continue to do so. You are near and dear to My heart and I have placed you on this earth for such a time as this. Remember that in the latter days, love will grow cold and wickedness will be on the rise. Do not fear; be strong and courageous. You will prevail if you will saturate yourself with My Holy Word and if, in all things, you respond in love. Life is like a winding road with ditches on both sides. One ditch represents outright rebellion and sin; the other represents your response to someone else's sin. Satan could care less what ditch he gets you into, as long as he can get you off the road. Guard your heart...

_____

_____

_____

_____

_____

_____

_____

_____

_____

_____

_____

_____

_____

_____

_____

_____

Search for the Lord and for his strength, and keep on searching.
1 Chronicles 16:11 NLT

GO AFTER HIM!

Precious Father,

I want more of You! Search me, Oh God, and know my heart. Test me and know my apprehensive thoughts. Tell me if there is any distasteful way in me. Lead me in Your everlasting way. Forgive me for dipping from a cup while the ocean remains! Your Word tells me that if I ask for more of You, I will receive it. So, Lord, I ask for more strength, more wisdom and more insight. I ask for a deeper love for Your Word and a profound understanding of Your heart for Your children. Show me...

_____

_____

_____

_____

_____

_____

_____

_____

_____

_____

_____

_____

_____

_____

Go After Him

My Treasured Child,

It is my great pleasure to answer your prayers. As I give you these things, I will also bring forth opportunities to represent Me to a lost and dying world. Remember, too, that the enemy will seek to test what's been planted, so stay close to Me and stand on My truths. You are loved; you are cared for but you cannot go it alone; be grounded in the Word of God. Quietly sit in My presence now as I show you the things I am planting in you...

_____

_____

_____

_____

_____

_____

_____

_____

_____

_____

_____

_____

_____

_____

_____

_____

_____

Through each day the Lord pours his unfailing love upon me,
and through each night I sing his songs, praying to God who gives me life.
Psalm 42:8 NLT

BREATHE...

Precious Lord,

Day by day, You pour Your love upon me...what a beautiful thought! You give me life and You love me beyond words. May my everyday, be an expression of Your love in and through me. As I breathe in the love You give, may I breathe out songs of praise, words of encouragement, and prayers of thanks. May my walk with You be natural and instinctive, just like the air I breathe. As I go about my day, let me hear Your voice...

_____

_____

_____

_____

_____

_____

_____

_____

_____

_____

_____

_____

_____

Breathe

Wonderful Child,

It is my great pleasure to lavish you with love. You are precious in My sight... every part of you. Sit with Me for a while and pour out your heart to Me. Let me hear what concerns you, what worries you, and what you're dreaming about. You talk and I'll listen. As you release your cares to Me, I will give you My peace and direction. You are rich beyond measure; I have given you...

_____

_____

_____

_____

_____

_____

_____

_____

_____

_____

_____

_____

_____

_____

_____

_____

_____

_____

Teach us to make the most of our time, so that we may grow in wisdom.
Psalm 90:12 NLT

SAVOR THE FLAVOR...

Awesome God,

Life gets moving so fast that I often forget to taste my food! Help me to slow down and take it all in. Help me to pause throughout the day and notice the sky You've painted, and to watch for a moment as the trees stir from an unseen wind. Help me to sneak a peek out of a high rise window and be amazed at how far I can see. I miss so much when I rush through life. You have given me this day as an amazing gift. May I return it to You at the end of the day, having enjoyed Your creation, having obeyed Your Word and having loved Your people. Today I thank You for...

_____

_____

_____

_____

_____

_____

_____

_____

_____

_____

_____

_____

_____

Savor the Flavor

Precious Child,

This is the abundant life! My fingerprints are everywhere; My beauty is written all over nature. Determine to live a life filled with moments where you pause...and take it all in. Your days will be brighter and your heart will be lighter. As you begin to value your life, you will gain wisdom for your calling. You are a treasure to Me beyond words! Look around you today and notice how I...

_____

_____

_____

_____

_____

_____

_____

_____

_____

_____

_____

_____

_____

_____

_____

_____

_____

_____

_____

...May the Lord our God show us his approval and make our efforts
successful. Yes, make our efforts successful!
Psalm 90:17 NLT

GODLY SUCCESS...

Precious Father,

*How great You are. This is Your show, Lord, not mine. Protect me from any
selfish ambition that would lead me away from Your Throne. Give me a heart
to do everything as an act of worship to You! With a humble heart I confess
that everything good comes from You. Open doors before me and establish the
work of my hands. Whether things are happening for me or not, Your Name
is to be praised! Your Word tells me that, as I delight myself in You, my
desires (which come from You) will be fulfilled...*

_____

_____

_____

_____

_____

_____

_____

_____

_____

_____

_____

_____

_____

Godly Success

Precious Child,

As you listen to My whisper in your heart and do the things I ask you to - you will become even more in tuned to My voice. My thoughts are always turned towards you. I love you and am always cheering for you. The more you understand your humble position before Me, the more I can trust you enough to lift you up and use you in powerful ways. As you have the courage to respond to My dealings with you, I will remove the veil from your eyes and you will see Me in a deeper way. You will see amazing things happen on your watch; you will see...

_____

_____

_____

_____

_____

_____

_____

_____

_____

_____

_____

_____

_____

_____

_____

_____

The Lord is a warrior; yes, the Lord is his name!
Exodus 15:3 NLT

A HOLY WARRIOR...

Mighty Father,

*You are not just the Lamb who was led to the slaughter – You are also a
powerful warrior who fights for the weak. You are strong and mighty.
Nothing is too hard for You. As a strategic commander, You rule the heavens
and send angels to fight for us daily. Help me to remember that I am equipped
for the battle You've called me to fight. Protect me from engaging in the wrong
battles. Let me not be distracted with petty issues when You have called me to
a more noble fight. Show me Your way for me...*

_____

_____

_____

_____

_____

_____

_____

_____

_____

_____

_____

_____

_____

_____

_____

A Holy Warrior

Warrior Child,

This is a very important request. In these latter days, you MUST remember that you are in a battle zone whether you want to be or not. With every step you take towards purity and holiness, you'll find the enemy waiting to destroy or distract you from advancement. Don't let this discourage you though; if you persevere in strength, humility and love, you will see miracles happen before your very eyes! Jesus is your example; heaven is your prize. Sit with Me now and let Me speak to your heart...

God can do anything, you know - far more than you could ever imagine
or guess or request in your wildest dreams! He does it not by pushing us
around but by working within us, his Spirit deeply and gently within us.
Ephesians 3:20 MSG

BEYOND OUR DREAMS...

Holy, Precious God,

*You are far above anything my little mind can comprehend. Oh how I love
you! May I never limit anything You want to do in or through me. Is there
anything in me that is a roadblock to You? Show me, Lord, how I can
cooperate with Your great plan for my life. Show me how I tend to get in the
way. Since You work gently, help me not to be headstrong. Show me the
vision that is beyond me - an assignment that requires You to be present in
my life...*

_____

_____

_____

_____

_____

_____

_____

_____

_____

_____

_____

_____

_____

_____

_____

Beyond Our Dreams

Precious Child,

I have crafted you and formed you for a very specific purpose. I have given you gifts, talents and desires. Some are undeveloped, some are untapped, but they are there and I am more than able to use them. It is My job to open doors, make connections and prepare you for service; it is yours to trust Me as I deal with you. Anyone who ever did anything great, was trained and strengthened while the world seemingly passed them by. Are you ready to see things change in your world? Trust me, obey me and stay close to Me. I want you to...

_____

_____

_____

_____

_____

_____

_____

_____

_____

_____

_____

_____

_____

_____

_____

_____

_____

_____

For God does speak--now one way, now another--
though man may not perceive it.
Job 33:14 NIV

GOD'S VOICE...

Precious Lord,

I want to hear Your voice; I know You whisper and the world shouts. I refuse to allow a relentless pace to dictate my life. I can't expect to hear anything from You if I won't first slow down enough to rest with You. Help me to value more and more, our time together. You speak to me in so many different ways and I don't want to miss a thing. Show me what in my hand needs to go, so I can take hold of more of You. Open my ears to that I can hear You speaking to me...

_____

_____

_____

_____

_____

_____

_____

_____

_____

_____

_____

_____

_____

God's Voice

Beloved Child,

Have you ever tried to share something intimate with someone while they were doing five other things? That's how I often feel when I am speaking to My children. I have such profound truths to share; I want to issue warnings and cautions for protection; I even want to commend acts done in love; and yet, so much is missed because endless tasks choke intimate times of fellowship. Remember, My Word says, as you develop a reverence for Me, I will confide in you. Ponder that for a moment – the God of the Universe wants to confide in you! I've wanted to tell you...

_____

_____

_____

_____

_____

_____

_____

_____

_____

_____

_____

_____

_____

_____

_____

_____

Let us see your miracles again; let our children see your glory at work.
Psalm 90:16 NLT

GOD'S POWER...

Father God,

I want more of You. Pour out Your Spirit upon me and on the ones that I love. Take me to the next place You have for me. Help me not to be an earthbound traveler but, rather, a heavenly-minded warrior carrying high the banner of love. May my life reflect Your power and may my choices reflect Your direction in my life. Give me the gift of faith for...

_____

_____

_____

_____

_____

_____

_____

_____

_____

_____

_____

_____

_____

_____

_____

God's Power

Wonderful Child,

As you draw near to Me, I will draw near to you. Keep reaching and you'll take hold of all that I have taken hold of for you. I will withhold no good thing from those who walk in a manner worthy of the calling. I delight to lavish upon you all you need to live a life bursting with the power of love. Take time to meditate on My ability to move mountains when it's called for. Meditate on My great power and your faith will grow...

_____

_____

_____

_____

_____

_____

_____

_____

_____

_____

_____

_____

_____

_____

_____

_____

_____

_____

_____

The Sovereign Lord has spoken to me, and I have listened.
I do not rebel or turn away.
Isaiah 50: 5 NLT

AN OBEDIENT HEART...

Fairest Lord Jesus,

How easy it is to depart from Your path and go my own way. Lord, help me not to do that. I want to do Your will, but so often my selfishness takes over. Speak to my heart again today and I will listen. Tell me what to do, what to say, and what in my life needs to go. I am convinced that Yours is the path of peace and security. Keep me close to Your heartbeat, Oh Lord; these are the things that sometimes veil my eyes from You...

An Obedient Heart

Precious, Precious Child,

I love a heart like yours. I am right here for you. I will teach you, guide you and counsel you in the way that you should go. Take time to just sit in My Presence until our hearts beat together with the same rhythm. The only way to defy the gravity of sin is by immersing yourself in My ways, My words and My wisdom. Meditate on Scripture, be faithful in prayer and don't let anything steal our time together...this is sacred time. Today, I want you to know...

_____

_____

_____

_____

_____

_____

_____

_____

_____

_____

_____

_____

_____

_____

_____

_____

_____

_____

He (Noah) consistently followed God's will and
enjoyed a close relationship with him.
Genesis 6:9b NLT

NEAR TO GOD...

Gracious Father,

*I want to enjoy a close relationship with You. Move in my soul so that my
affections match Yours. Give me a heart for Your desires. Open the eyes of my
heart so that I may see the world in the way that You do. Protect me from
living the selfish life; I want to live for You. Show me, today, what tendencies
I have that may block my intimacy with You...*

_____

_____

_____

_____

_____

_____

_____

_____

_____

_____

_____

_____

_____

_____

Near to God

Sweet, Sweet Child,

I love you. Do you know that? I really love you. As you sit quietly in My presence, I will pour My love on you. I will place in your heart a desire to bring My love to a lost world. Listen to Me now as I speak to you. Quietly listen. Do you hear My voice in your heart? My will for you today is...

_____

_____

_____

_____

_____

_____

_____

_____

_____

_____

_____

_____

_____

_____

_____

_____

_____

_____

_____

_____

_____

Then Moses said, "If you don't go with us personally,
don't let us move a step from this place."
Exodus 33:15 NLT

IN STEP WITH HIM...

Holy Father,

More than anything, I want to stay in step with You. I tend to set my mind on the things I want while missing the things I need. Don't let me depart from the path of righteousness. I only want to be where You are. Protect me Lord, from hasty decisions. May Your voice be what guides me. Show me the way that I should go...

_____

_____

_____

_____

_____

_____

_____

_____

_____

_____

_____

_____

_____

_____

_____

_____

In Step With Him

Precious Child,

I am never in a hurry; I'm always on time. Do not let yourself be rushed into a decision; do not make big decisions while you are running uphill or while you are crawling through a crisis. I am not in a hurry and I am in control. Even if you don't feel that you do - you have enough time to come before Me for wisdom and direction, and you have enough time to wait for My answer. Determine to believe that your life is of such great value that I will guide you and My Presence will go with you. You are not left to figure things out on your own...

_____

_____

_____

_____

_____

_____

_____

_____

_____

_____

_____

_____

_____

_____

_____

_____

_____

I lift my eyes to you, O God, enthroned in heaven. We look to the Lord
our God for his mercy, just as servants keep their eyes on their master,
as a slave girl watches her mistress for the slightest signal.
Psalm 123:1-2 NLT

AT HIS SERVICE...

Fairest Lord Jesus,

*As I imagine back in Your day, I picture a servant girl waiting with
anticipation for the first sign of need or direction from her mistress. Since the
psalmist made the connection between that servant girl and me, I know it
requires my attention. Help me to wait on You with that kind of anticipation,
knowing full well that You'll point to a need or direct me where I should
go. If I've given You my life, I must not live like I am my own master. I am
Your servant, Lord. Continue to work in me a heart to do Your will. I am here
today, Lord, what would You have me do?*

_____

_____

_____

_____

_____

_____

_____

_____

_____

_____

_____

_____

At His Service

Sweet, Sweet Child,

How I love your precious heart! You are my pride and joy and I'm so thankful to call you My own. More than anything, I want from you, a yielded, humble, trusting heart. It is when My children get demanding or feel entitled that they become blinded to what they already have. As you embrace your fragility before Me, I will make you powerful for Me. Today, it would please My heart intensely if you would...

_____

_____

_____

_____

_____

_____

_____

_____

_____

_____

_____

_____

_____

_____

_____

_____

_____

_____

_____

You gave me life and showed me your unfailing love.
My life was preserved by your care.
Job 10:12 NLT

MY SOURCE...

Holy Father,

You are my Source of life. You are the reason I live and move and have my being. You have saved me from death and You will protect me in times of trouble. You watch me closely and You counsel me with Your eye on me. As beautiful as Your gifts are, they don't replace You. They never could. May I never chase after the gifts of Your hand more than I pursue the presence of Your heart. As I come before You, show me the sources I've been looking to instead of You (and as you show me, forgive me)...

_____

_____

_____

_____

_____

_____

_____

_____

_____

_____

_____

_____

_____

_____

My Source

Treasured Child,

You are My prized possession. You can only imagine how it breaks My heart when you draw from muddy puddles when I have a fresh spring for you! Everything that comes from My hand will fill, heal and equip you for life. You cannot satisfy your soul the way that I can. My resources are inexhaustible and I will open heaven's storehouse to the asking heart. Ask Me now for...

_____

_____

_____

_____

_____

_____

_____

_____

_____

_____

_____

_____

_____

_____

_____

_____

_____

_____

_____

His great works are too marvelous to understand.
He performs miracles without number.
Job 9:10 NLT

MIGHTY GOD...

Holy Father,

I come before You today, Lord, just to be in Your presence. Your ways are far higher than mine. Your thoughts are beautiful and holy. Your kindness and grace abound and are so undeserved. And yet I stretch my arms open wide and I receive all You have for me with reckless abandon. I open up the depths of my soul and allow You to heal and restore me in the deepest places. There is no one like You, and You are my God. I could fill pages telling You who You are to me...

_____

_____

_____

_____

_____

_____

_____

_____

_____

_____

_____

_____

_____

_____

Mighty God

Precious Child,

Oh, how I love you, too! Now I get to tell you who you are to Me. You are My prized possession. I love how I made you and I love it when you trust Me. I love it when you laugh; it makes Me laugh, too. I hear it when you pray as you go about your day (and keep praying by the way; your prayers are changing things). I see it when you give away your share and My heart swells with pride. You are mine. I am very glad to call you My own. When I look upon your heart, I see...

_____

_____

_____

_____

_____

_____

_____

_____

_____

_____

_____

_____

_____

_____

_____

_____

Because of our faith, Christ has brought us into this place of highest privilege
where we now stand,
and we confidently and joyfully look forward to sharing God's glory.
Romans 5:2 NLT

WHERE WE STAND...

Mighty Lord,

*To think that right now, in the land of the living, I stand in the place of
highest privilege with You. This is almost too much to comprehend! Help me
not to take this promise lightly, but to meditate on it day and night. Help me,
Jesus, not to just scratch the surface with the things You want to do in and
through me. Grant me faith and insight to believe it when You say that
You'll move mountains on my behalf. Stir in my soul right now and show me
how to abide in this place of highest privilege...*

_____

_____

_____

_____

_____

_____

_____

_____

_____

_____

_____

Where We Stand

My Redeemed Child,

How I wish that all My children were in hot pursuit of this truth. The gates of hell cannot prevail against an army of saints who believe in their high standing. If you knew of all the untapped resources in heaven, you would be shaken to your core. As you humble yourself and develop a holy fear before Me, I will lift you up, confide in you and tell you things you do not know. You are Mine and we will work together to change the world. Always remember...

_____

_____

_____

_____

_____

_____

_____

_____

_____

_____

_____

_____

_____

_____

_____

_____

Lord, teach us to pray.
Luke 11:1 NIV

PRAYER...

Holy Lord,

Everything about You is beyond my limited mind's grasp. And yet I search and long for You more than anything else. Help me to plumb the depths as I pray. Show me what kinds of prayers please You most. Give me discernment so that my prayers will foil the plans of the enemy. Make me stronger, wiser and more loving in my prayers. Expand my vision so that my prayers don't just revolve around me. Remind me to pray for my suffering brothers and sisters around the world. Show me, Lord...

_____

_____

_____

_____

_____

_____

_____

_____

_____

_____

_____

_____

_____

_____

_____

Prayer

Beloved Child,

*I will answer your prayers. Soon, you will find us talking all day long!
Remember, when you're praying, keep Me in mind. If your focus is on your
mountain, your faith will be small. But if your eyes are on Me, your mountain
won't seem impassable. Every time you respond to My voice, I will reveal
more of Myself to you. As you grow in your love and reverence of Me, I will
tell you deep and wonderful truths. If you want power in your family, city
and church - pray. To put forth prayer is to put forth power. Our connection
will keep you anchored when the storms rage. Your prayers are your lifeline
to Me. Let's keep talking...*

_____

_____

_____

_____

_____

_____

_____

_____

_____

_____

_____

_____

_____

_____

_____

_____

_____

_____

Your eyes are windows into your body. If you open your eyes wide in wonder and belief, your body fills up with light. If you live squinty-eyed in greed and distrust, your body is a dank cellar. If you pull the blinds on your windows, what a dark life you will have!
Matthew 6:22-23 MSG

OPEN MY EYES...

Oh Lord,

This world is polluted with sin and it's difficult at times to keep that wide-eyed wonder You have called me to. And yet, when I lift my eyes to the hills, I know where my help comes from. My help comes from You, the Maker of heaven and earth. Heighten my conviction so that I will be unable to look upon things that are in contrast to Your holiness; purify my mind so that I my Spirit-eyes will be open wide. My eyes are the filter to my soul; help me to see Your...

_____

_____

_____

_____

_____

_____

_____

_____

_____

_____

_____

_____

_____

Open My Eyes

Beloved Child,

I am here for you. So many times throughout your day, I long to put My hand under your chin and lift it to look upon My face. All of your fears will fade away as you gaze upon My holiness. It is true, you are surrounded by dirty writing on the walls, and yet I say that you can still come through this life with more purity than when you started. What you look for, you will find. If you are determined to find Me, you will. If you are bent on noticing what's wrong with every situation, you'll find that too. I want you to focus on...

_____

_____

_____

_____

_____

_____

_____

_____

_____

_____

_____

_____

_____

_____

_____

_____

_____

Seek the Lord while you can find him. Call on him now while he is near.
Isaiah 55:6 NLT

SEEK HIM FIRST...

Faithful Father,

I must confess, so often I find myself looking for things and people to satisfy my deepest needs. Forgive me for being so shortsighted. Lord, You alone were meant to complete me and fill me up. Why do I spend time grasping for things that You freely give? Help me, Father, to think of You first, to run to You first and to remember that You are the Source of everything I need. Forgive me, Lord - these are the things and people that I have looked to, to fill me...

_____

_____

_____

_____

_____

_____

_____

_____

_____

_____

_____

_____

_____

_____

Seek Him First

Sweet Child,

My heart aches when My children believe a lie. There are so many awesome things I want you to do...but filling yourself is not one of them. If the devil can get you to believe wrongly about yourself, he will be able to disrupt every area of your life. On the other hand, if you can believe Me when I say this: you are valuable, irreplaceable and I love you - then you will live life out of fullness. Determine to come to Me every time you doubt, every time you're afraid, every time you even wonder who you are and what you're supposed to be doing. I love you and I...

And I ask him that with both feet planted firmly on love, you'll be able to take in with all Christians the extravagant dimensions of Christ's love. Reach out and experience the breadth! Test its length! Plumb the depths! Rise to the heights! Live full lives, full to the fullness of God.
Ephesians 3:14-19 MSG

GOD'S RECKLESS LOVE...

Awesome and Loving Father,

I am done with scratching the surface and marginal living! I want to jump in and swim in the ocean of Your love! Help me, transform me and get rid of anything in me that would hinder my capacity to fully enjoy Your abounding Presence! Your love is so unfair, so undeserved; it spills over the edges and reaches the lowest places. It goes deeper than any pain, any sin and any secret. As I put aside earthbound living, I wrap myself around a Spirit-filled life. I stretch my arms open wide Lord; pour out Your Spirit upon me and teach me...

_____

_____

_____

_____

_____

_____

_____

_____

_____

_____

_____

_____

_____

God's Reckless Love

Precious Child,

Oh, how I love a request like yours! You cannot exhaust My supply, nor can you get enough of Me; so don't stop searching, reaching and pressing in to Me. One thing is for sure: many of My children will walk through heaven's gates and will instantly realize all of the resources that were left untapped. You don't want to do that. Ask for more faith, more wisdom, and ask for a greater vision for your life. I love to give to those who ask of Me. Ask Me now for...

_____

_____

_____

_____

_____

_____

_____

_____

_____

_____

_____

_____

_____

_____

_____

_____

_____

_____